What to do when you can't multiply and divide

By
Steve Chinn

Egon Publishers Ltd

What to do when you can't multiply and divide

Published 2009
Egon Publishers Ltd
618 Leeds Road, Outwood
Wakefield WF1 2LT

Tel/FAX: 01924 871697

www.egon.co.uk
information@egon.co.uk

ISBN: 978 1904160 96 0

There are 5 books in this series : –

What to do when you can't tell the time
What to do when you can't add and subtract
What to do when you can't multiply and divide
What to do when you can't do the times tables
What to do when you can't do fractions, decimals and percentages

Typeset by Omega Cottage DTP & Web Design
Tingley, Wakefield

ABOUT THIS BOOK

This book is one of a series of books which have been written to make maths and numbers easier to remember, use and understand. The skills and the needs of learners who find maths difficult have been major influences in how these books are constructed.

The books take a fresh look at maths skills, helping many more people to understand the patterns and links that make learning more successful.

This whole book, even if not a very big one, has been devoted to two maths operations, multiplication and division which create much anxiety in too many learners. Anxiety leads to stress and sets the seeds that grow into a lack of confidence with maths and numbers.

This book offers an alternative approach to mastering these operations. It is not a magic cure, nor a quick fix. It will involve effort and a lot of practise, but it does acknowledge that the facts that people can access are often restricted to 1x, 2x, 5x and 10x and uses these to help make the processes of multiplication and division easier and more successful. It makes that restricted range of fact retrieval into a strength.

The same ideas and principles are used in all the 'What to do...' books. These ideas link together, building skills and understanding. The principles are based on making learning match the learner.

If you have memories, however recent or distant, of methods that were meaningless, confusing and unsuccessful, then the explanations and methods in this book will show you that there are ways to succeed. Being unable to remember how to use the traditional methods is not a problem if you can understand and use viable alternative methods. Understanding will always beat recall.

Steve Chinn

Section

1

MULTIPLICATION

Why do learners get confused about multiplication?

The reasons include:

- Confusing language
- Poor understanding of place value
- The order/sequence of working with the numbers
- A weak understanding of what multiplication means
- A limited recall/retrieval of basic multiplication facts
- Fear of failure
- Inability to check or appraise answers

Each 'What to do...' book is a part of a structure that aims to make maths skills more accessible.

This is achieved by:

- Using number facts that most people can recall/retrieve
- Introducing understandable ways to tackle maths procedures
- Linking these ways so that each way supports and develops old skills into new skills

The structure explained in this and the other books in the series is built on learning principles which have been chosen because they support the learner and reduce the chances of errors, failures and de-motivation. The structure takes the core principles of maths and uses them to link new topics to old topics.

Basic multiplication facts, the times tables, are dealt with in a book of their own *What to do when you can't learn the times tables.*

Building a foundation

Multiplication is often considered by learners to be the second hardest of the four operations on numbers. The four operations are addition, subtraction, multiplication and division and are called 'operations' because they are how we work on, or operate on, numbers.

- For addition we are putting numbers together
- For subtraction we are separating numbers
- For multiplication we are combining (or adding) several of the same number
- For division we are taking away several of the same number, separating the starting number into equal groups

Let's look at some examples:

Addition Addition is a sub-skill for multiplication. The following activities offer a brief review of this skill.

15 add 10. 15 + 10. We put together, or add, 15 and 10 to get 25.

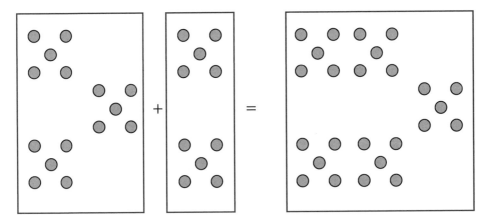

ACTIVITY M1   Practising addition. The pattern of adding 10

Start with ten coins or counters set out in the five pattern.

Write   10 +   next to the coins/counters.

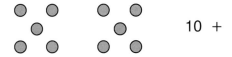

10 +

Now set out 4 coins (or counters) next to the ten coins and write 4 as shown.

10 + 4

Count the coins/counters and write the total   ……………
Check that your answer is correct. If not, try re-counting, starting to count after 10, eleven, twelve, thirteen, fourteen.

Now, to set up the next example, remove the group of 4 coins (counters) and replace them with 6 coins (counters) so that you have 10 + 6.

10 + 6

Write the total number of coins (counters)   ……
Check that your answer is correct. The answer should be sixteen (16).
If you obtained a different answer then ask for assistance.

5

Repeat this activity for:

10 + 2	....
10 + 3	....
10 + 4	14
10 + 5	....
10 + 6	16
10 + 7	....
10 + 8	....
10 + 9	....

Can you see a pattern in the numbers in your answers?

How would that pattern change and what would the answers be if you were adding onto 11 instead of 10?

11 + 2	....
11 + 3	....
11 + 4	....
11 + 5	....
11 + 6	....
11 + 7	....
11 + 8	....
11 + 9	....

Make sure you use coins for the last example, using the fives patterns, even if you have felt confident enough not to use them for the previous examples.

Now look at the pattern when you add onto 9. Compare it to the pattern of adding onto 10.

$$9 + 2 \qquad \ldots\ldots\ldots$$
$$9 + 3 \qquad \ldots\ldots\ldots$$
$$9 + 4 \qquad \ldots\ldots\ldots$$
$$9 + 5 \qquad \ldots\ldots\ldots$$
$$9 + 6 \qquad \ldots\ldots\ldots$$
$$9 + 7 \qquad \ldots\ldots\ldots$$
$$9 + 8 \qquad \ldots\ldots\ldots$$
$$9 + 9 \qquad \ldots\ldots\ldots$$

You can use coins to show how this pattern develops from the 10+ pattern.

If you set up the coins to show 9 + 4, then move one coin to make the 9 up to 10, this changes the addition into 10 + 3.

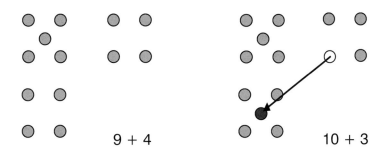

9 + 4   10 + 3

ACTIVITY M2 Adding with 'carrying' or 'trading'. e.g. 46 + 16

The next activities use 10p and 1p coins to demonstrate place value issues. (Where 1p stands for one unit and thus 10p for 10 units.)

The first activity in this part is to demonstrate the need to 'trade' (or 'carry') ten 1p coins for one 10p coin.

Set up 46 and 16:

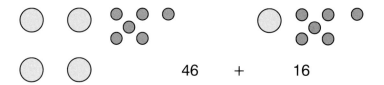

46   +   16

Now add them together. There are twelve 1p coins. Trade ten 1p coins for one 10p coin, so that 50 + 12 becomes 62

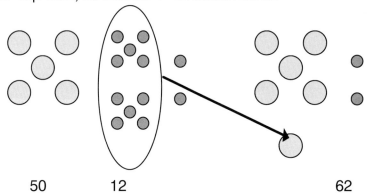

50   12   62

Set up other examples for the learner.

If the learner is not able to do these successfully, then return to the programme in *'What to do when you can't add and subtract.'*

Worksheet M1 provides a further check of the ability to add.

WORKSHEET M1 Addition

1) 35 + 10 =

2) 35 + 9 =

3) 35 + 8 =

4) 44 + 6 =

5) 46 + 4 =

6) 46 + 5 =

7) 68 + 8 =

8) 27 + 7 =

9) 76 + 6 =

10) 68 + 18 =

11) 27 + 17 =

12) 76 + 16 =

13)
$$\begin{array}{r} 76 \\ + 13 \\ \hline \end{array}$$

14)
$$\begin{array}{r} 37 \\ + 28 \\ \hline \end{array}$$

15)
$$\begin{array}{r} 56 \\ + 38 \\ \hline \end{array}$$

16)
$$\begin{array}{r} 354 \\ + 445 \\ \hline \end{array}$$

17)
$$\begin{array}{r} 508 \\ + 163 \\ \hline \end{array}$$

18)
$$\begin{array}{r} 737 \\ + 174 \\ \hline \end{array}$$

(Note: The questions are set to explore patterns and to be diagnostic of addition errors. Should a learner achieve a low score, then Worksheet M2 can be used as a post-intervention check). If the learner is not able to do these second examples successfully, then return to the programme in 'What to do when you can't add and subtract'. Addition is a pre-requisite skill for multiplication and for some division procedures. ,

WORKSHEET M2 Addition

1) $56 + 10 =$ 2) $56 + 9 =$

3) $56 + 8 =$ 4) $33 + 7 =$

5) $37 + 3 =$ 6) $37 + 4 =$

7) $78 + 8 =$ 8) $47 + 7 =$

9) $26 + 6 =$ 10) $38 + 28 =$

11) $57 + 37 =$ 12) $26 + 46 =$

13) $\begin{array}{r} 52 \\ + 16 \\ \hline \end{array}$ 14) $\begin{array}{r} 68 \\ + 27 \\ \hline \end{array}$

15) $\begin{array}{r} 76 \\ + 18 \\ \hline \end{array}$ 16) $\begin{array}{r} 251 \\ + 437 \\ \hline \end{array}$

17) $\begin{array}{r} 308 \\ + 374 \\ \hline \end{array}$ 18) $\begin{array}{r} 649 \\ + 252 \\ \hline \end{array}$

Subtraction

Subtraction is another sub-skill for multiplication and division.

30 subtract 20. 30 – 20. We start with 30 and take away 20 to get 10.

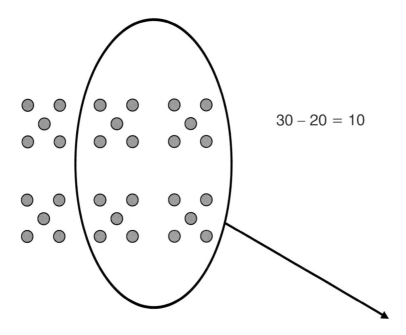

$$30 - 20 = 10$$

ACTIVITY M3

We start using only 1p coins. These activities look at subtraction as 'taking away', as counting back and then by counting on.

The first activity is to use coins to work out 13 – 4. Set up 13 coins using the 'five' pattern. Then take away 4 coins (shaded black in the second diagram). The answer, 9, could be obtained by counting back from 13:

    .... 12 ... 11 ... 10 ... 9, and the layout of the coins could be used to demonstrate that strategy.

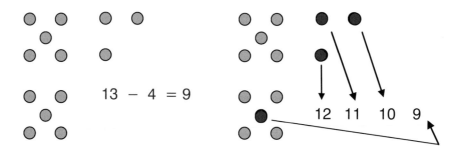

The layout could be used to show how counting on from 4 to 13 would also give an answer of 9. So, 4...

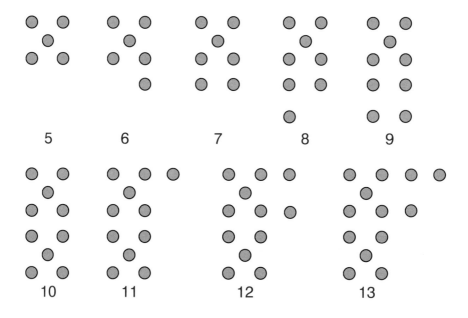

Set up another similar example and check if the learner can do the activities correctly.

The next activities use 10p and 1p coins to demonstrate place value issues.

The first activity in this part is to demonstrate the need to 'trade' (or 'decompose' or 'rename') one 10p into ten 1p coins.

Set up 34, ready for the subtraction of 16:   34 – 16

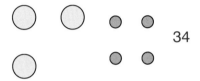

34

Discuss with the learner how six 1p coins could be subtracted/taken away when there are only four. Show how trading one of the 10p coins can generate an extra ten 1p coins whilst still leaving the total value as 34p.

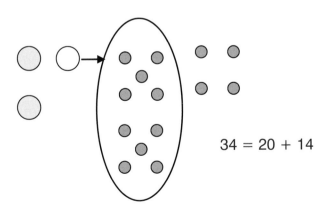

34 = 20 + 14

Now take away 16p as one 10p and six 1p coins (shaded black), leaving 18p. Show how this is written in vertical form.

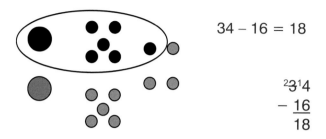

$$34 - 16 = 18$$

$$^2\text{З}^14$$
$$- \ 16$$
$$\overline{18}$$

It may help some learners to use an intermediate line to show the trading more explicitly:

$$
\begin{array}{r}
3 \ \ 4 \\
2 \ 14 \\
-1 \ \ 6 \\
\hline
1 \ \ 8
\end{array}
$$
2 tens and 14 ones

Set up 56 and ask the learner to take away 27 by using trading. Show how this is written out.

If the learner is not able to do this successfully, then return to the programme in 'What to do when you can't add and subtract'.

Worksheet M3 provides a further check of the ability to subtract.

WORKSHEET M3

1) $8 - 7 =$

2) $18 - 7 =$

3) $68 - 27 =$

4) $16 - 9 =$

5) $26 - 9 =$

6) $36 - 19 =$

7) $\begin{array}{r} 68 \\ - 37 \\ \hline \end{array}$

8) $\begin{array}{r} 68 \\ - 38 \\ \hline \end{array}$

9) $\begin{array}{r} 68 \\ - 39 \\ \hline \end{array}$

10) $\begin{array}{r} 88 \\ - 28 \\ \hline \end{array}$

11) $\begin{array}{r} 89 \\ - 28 \\ \hline \end{array}$

12) $\begin{array}{r} 90 \\ - 28 \\ \hline \end{array}$

13) $\begin{array}{r} 853 \\ - 637 \\ \hline \end{array}$

14) $\begin{array}{r} 715 \\ - 543 \\ \hline \end{array}$

15) $\begin{array}{r} 237 \\ - 138 \\ \hline \end{array}$

16) $\begin{array}{r} 460 \\ - 128 \\ \hline \end{array}$

17) $\begin{array}{r} 702 \\ - 361 \\ \hline \end{array}$

18) $\begin{array}{r} 600 \\ - 173 \\ \hline \end{array}$

(Note: The questions are set to explore patterns and to be diagnostic of subtraction errors. Should a learner achieve a low score, then Worksheet M4 can be used as a post-intervention check). If the learner is not able to do these second examples successfully, then return to the programme in 'What to do when you can't add and subtract'. Subtraction is a pre-requisite skill for division and for some multiplication procedures.

WORKSHEET M4

1) $7 - 6 =$ 2) $17 - 6 =$

3) $67 - 26 =$ 4) $14 - 9 =$

5) $24 - 9 =$ 6) $34 - 19 =$

7) $\begin{array}{r} 67 \\ -\ 47 \\ \hline \end{array}$ 8) $\begin{array}{r} 67 \\ -\ 48 \\ \hline \end{array}$ 9) $\begin{array}{r} 67 \\ -\ 49 \\ \hline \end{array}$

10) $\begin{array}{r} 68 \\ -\ 18 \\ \hline \end{array}$ 11) $\begin{array}{r} 69 \\ -\ 18 \\ \hline \end{array}$ 12) $\begin{array}{r} 70 \\ -\ 18 \\ \hline \end{array}$

13) $\begin{array}{r} 874 \\ -\ 326 \\ \hline \end{array}$ 14) $\begin{array}{r} 626 \\ -\ 283 \\ \hline \end{array}$ 15) $\begin{array}{r} 443 \\ -\ 244 \\ \hline \end{array}$

16) $\begin{array}{r} 380 \\ -\ 127 \\ \hline \end{array}$ 17) $\begin{array}{r} 804 \\ -\ 432 \\ \hline \end{array}$ 18) $\begin{array}{r} 800 \\ -\ 287 \\ \hline \end{array}$

MULTIPLICATION

What is multiplication?

Start by looking at an example: 6 times 10. 6 x 10.

We can use repeated (multi) addition and add 6 lots of 10 to get 60.

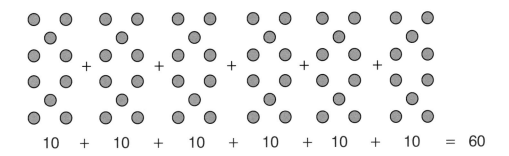

10 + 10 + 10 + 10 + 10 + 10 = 60

Multiplication is related to addition, so our 6 x 10 is actually 10 + 10 + 10 + 10 + 10 + 10, that is 6 additions of 10. So we say that multiplication is a repeated addition of the same number. In this example we repeated the addition of 10.

We can use 'lots of' to infer multiplication by repeated addition. So '1 lot of 10' can be pictured as:

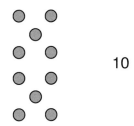

10

'2 lots of 10' is

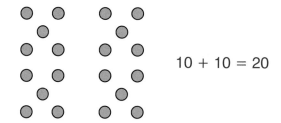

$$10 + 10 = 20$$

There is full coverage of basic multiplication facts in *'What to do when you can't learn the times tables'*.

Vocabulary

Several other words are used to mean multiplication and multiply. We have already met 'lots of'. We also use 'times' and, especially when multiplication involves decimals, fractions and percentages, we use 'of'.

'Lots of' does have a meaning related to what it says.
'Times' is abstract in terms of its mathematical use. It is also used (confusingly) in non-mathematical contexts ('good and bad times').
'Of' is just strange! It probably relates to 'lots of'.

Words: multiply   times   lots of   of   product

And sometimes no word, as in 'three nines' or 'six sevens'.

ACTIVITY M4

Demonstrate the 2x multiplication facts as repeated addition with base ten blocks (or with coins):

1 x 2 = 2	▭	2
2 x 2 = 4	▭ ▭	2 + 2
3 x 2 = 6	▭ ▭ ▭	2 + 2 + 2
4 x 2 = 8	▭ ▭ ▭ ▭	2 + 2 + 2 + 2
5 x 2 = 10	▭ ▭ ▭ ▭ ▭	2 + 2 + 2 + 2 + 2

Multiplication is meant to make repeated addition more efficient, mainly by being a quicker procedure. Also, it is often the case that if we can reduce the number of steps, we can reduce the number of chances for errors to occur.

However, repeated addition need not always be done in one step. In fact, as the problems get harder most people have to use two or more steps. The trick is to make the number of steps efficient for the task and the learner, a compromise depending on the individual.

Repeated addition can be made more efficient by grouping the numbers. For example,

$$17 \times 7 \quad \text{or} \quad 17 \text{ lots of } 7$$

$$7 + 7 + 7 + 7 + 7 + 7 + 7 + 7 + 7 + 7 + 7 + 7 + 7 + 7 + 7 + 7 + 7$$

We can group the 17 lots of 7 into 10 lots of 7, 5 lots of 7 and 2 lots of 7. Many people find that 10, 5 and 2 are the multipliers that they find the easiest to use.

So our grouping looks like:

$$(7 + 7 + 7 + 7 + 7 + 7 + 7 + 7 + 7 + 7) \; + \; (7 + 7 + 7 + 7 + 7) \; + \; (7 + 7)$$

This is   10 x 7   +   5 x 7   +   2 x 7

which is   70   +   35   +   14

$$17 \times 7 = 119$$

ACTIVITY M5

Again, demonstrate the 2x multiplication facts with base ten blocks (or with coins):

1 x 2 = 2		2
2 x 2 = 4		2 + 2
3 x 2 = 6		2 + 2 + 2
4 x 2 = 8		2 + 2 + 2 + 2
5 x 2 = 10		2 + 2 + 2 + 2 + 2

Now trade the 10 unit blocks for 1 ten block

5 x 2 = 10

10

So 10 x 2 would be

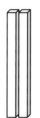

20

21

WORKSHEET M5

Practise grouping and adding. Circle all the 'easy (10, 5 and 2)
groups' for example 10 lots of a number

1) $\overbrace{4 + 4 + 4 + 4 + 4 + 4 + 4 + 4 + 4 + 4}$ + $\overbrace{4 + 4 + 4 + 4 + 4 + 4 + 4 + 4 + 4 + 4}$

10 x 4	+	10 x 4
40	+	40 = 80

2) 4 + 4 + 4 + 4 + 4 + 4 + 4 + 4 + 4 + 4 + 4 + 4

3) 5 + 5 + 5 + 5 + 5 + 5 + 5 + 5 + 5 + 5 + 5 + 5 + 5 + 5 + 5

4) 5 + 5 + 5 + 5 + 5 + 5 + 5

5) 5 + 5 + 5 + 5 + 5 + 5 + 5 + 5 + 5 + 5 + 5 + 5 + 5 + 5 + 5 + 5 + 5
    + 5 + 5 + 5 + 5 + 5

6) 7 + 7 + 7 + 7 + 7 + 7 + 7 + 7 + 7 + 7 + 7

7) 7 + 7 + 7 + 7 + 7 + 7 + 7 + 7 + 7 + 7 + 7 + 7 + 7 + 7 + 7

8) 12 + 12 + 12 + 12 + 12 + 12 + 12 + 12 + 12 + 12 + 12 + 12

9) 34 + 34 + 34 + 34 + 34 + 34 + 34 + 34 + 34 + 34 + 34

Grouping can be extended to big numbers by using:

   20x   50x   100x   200x   500x   1000x   and so on.

*A key skill is finding the 'easy' numbers in any multiplying number.
There are reasons to focus on the 'easy' numbers. One is an
increased chance of accuracy and the other is increased confidence.*

WORKSHEET M6   Finding the key numbers

The key numbers are: 1 2 5 10 20 50 100 200   and so on.

Examples: The key numbers in 16 are: 10 + 5 + 1

The key numbers in 136 are: 100 + 20 + 10 + 5 + 1

Find the key numbers in these numbers.

   1) 25   2) 120   3) 53

*** *make sure that questions 1, 2 and 3 are correct before you carry on* ***

   4) 27   5) 125   6) 56

   7) 28   8) 127   9) 57

   10) 9   11) 129   12) 506

When multipliers get bigger it is helpful to set up a table of key values, for example:

For   87 x 32   you will need:

$$87 \times 1 = 87$$
$$87 \times 2 = 174$$
$$87 \times 5 = 435$$
$$87 \times 10 = 870$$
$$87 \times 20 = 1740$$

Hint 1:
Sometimes it is easier to work out 5x values by halving the 10x value.
For example :

$$10 \times 87 = 870 \qquad 870 \div 2 = 435$$

This strategy can also be used to check the 5x answer.

Hint 2:
There are patterns in the values worked out in the table, for example:

$$1 \times 87 = 87 \quad \text{and} \quad 10 \times 87 = 870$$
$$2 \times 87 = 174 \quad \text{and} \quad 20 \times 87 = 1740$$

To multiply 87 by 32 in 'easy groups', we can break down the 32 into 20, 10 and 2.

32 lots of 87 is calculated as:

'20 lots of 87' **plus** '10 lots of 87' **plus** '2 lots of 87'

Add together the component multiples:

$$
\begin{array}{rr}
\mathbf{20} \times 87 = & 1740 \\
\mathbf{10} \times 87 = & 870 \\
\underline{\mathbf{2} \times 87 =} & \underline{174} \\
\mathbf{32} \times 87 = & 2784
\end{array}
$$

Another example: 26 x 87

The easy groups in 26 are

'20 lots of' **plus** '5 lots of' **plus** '1 lot of'

$$
\begin{array}{rr}
\mathbf{20} \times 87 = & 1740 \\
\mathbf{5} \times 87 = & 435 \\
\underline{\mathbf{1} \times 87 =} & \underline{87} \\
\mathbf{26} \times 87 = & 2262
\end{array}
$$

24

WORKSHEET M7   Setting up key value tables

Example: Setting up a key values table for 37.

$$37 \times 1 = 37$$
$$37 \times 2 = 74$$
$$37 \times 5 = 185$$
$$37 \times 10 = 370$$
$$37 \times 20 = 740$$
$$37 \times 50 = 1850$$
$$37 \times 100 = 3700$$

Remember to do the checks by looking at related values. In this 37 example it could be by comparing:

37 x 2 and 37 x 20   or   37 x 10 and 37 x 5

Find some other related pairs of key values.

Complete the following tables of key values from 1 x to 100x:

1)   21 x   1 = 21   2)   43 x   1 =
       21 x   2 =   43 x   2 =
       21 x   5 =   43 x   5 = 215
       21 x   10 =   43 x   10 =
       21 x   20 = 420   43 x   20 =
       21 x   50 =   43 x   50 =
       21 x 100 =   43 x 100 =

*** make sure that questions 1 and 2 are correct before you carry on ***

Practice writing out the key values for the following numbers:

   3) 33   4) 19

   5) 47   6) 57

WORKSHEET M8

Use the key values tables from WORKSHEET M 7 to work out:

   1) 37 x 45   2) 57 x 53

*****Make sure you have checked that questions 1 and 2 are correct before you move on to questions 3 to 6 *****

   3) 19 x 23   4) 33 x 32

   5) 43 x 75   6) 21 x 71

Dealing with 9 and 8

Nine and eight are close to ten and could be treated as a variation of the 'easy groups' method. This alternative involves subtraction. In the addition method we view 9 as:

$$9 = 5 + 2 + 2$$

In the subtraction alternative, we view 9 as:

$$9 = 10 - 1$$

In the addition method we view 8 as:

$$8 = 5 + 2 + 1$$

In the subtraction alternative, we view 8 as:

$$8 = 10 - 2$$

This alternative can be applied to any number with 8 or 9 in the digits place.

For example: 21 x 49

Set up the key values table:

$$
\begin{aligned}
1 \times 21 &= 21 \\
2 \times 21 &= 42 \\
5 \times 21 &= 105 \\
10 \times 21 &= 210 \\
20 \times 21 &= 420 \\
50 \times 21 &= 1050
\end{aligned}
$$

The key numbers in 49 are $50 - 1$, so the multiplication is:

$$
\begin{array}{cc}
\mathbf{50} \times 21 & 1050 \\
-\ 1 \times 21 & -\ \ 21 \\
\hline
49 \times 21 & 1029
\end{array}
$$

27

WORKSHEET M9

$$1 \times 37 = \quad 37$$
$$2 \times 37 = \quad 74$$
$$5 \times 37 = \quad 185$$
$$10 \times 37 = \quad 370$$
$$20 \times 37 = \quad 740$$
$$50 \times 37 = \quad 1850$$
$$100 \times 37 = \quad 3700$$

$$1 \times 21 = \quad 21$$
$$2 \times 21 = \quad 42$$
$$5 \times 21 = \quad 105$$
$$10 \times 21 = \quad 210$$
$$20 \times 21 = \quad 420$$
$$50 \times 21 = \quad 1050$$
$$100 \times 21 = \quad 2100$$

Use the key values above to calculate:

1)   37 x 19   2)   37 x 48   3)   37 x 99

4)   21 x 27   5)   21 x 18   6)   21 x 98

Traditional method for multiplication

The groups method above is very similar to the traditional method. It differs in how we break down the multiplier. In the example on page 23, (87 x 32), the multiplier or the multiplying number was 32. It was broken down into 20 and 10 and 2.

The question was to find 32 lots of 87, or 87 added together 32 times. We collected these 32 numbers into three groups based on easy multiplications. Sometimes this splitting of the multiplying number is called partitioning.

In the traditional method the multiplying number is partitioned into the tens and units of the number, in this case, 30 and 2.

The two multiples used in the calculation are 30x 87 and 2x 87.

This is 30 lots of 87 plus 2 lots of 87.

$$
\begin{array}{rcl}
\mathbf{30} \times 87 &=& 2610 \\
\underline{\mathbf{2} \times 87} &=& \underline{174} \\
\mathbf{32} \times 87 &=& 2784
\end{array}
$$

However, the layout used for this method is often more abstract:

$$
\begin{array}{r}
87 \\
\times\ 32 \\
\hline
2610 \\
\underline{174} \\
2784
\end{array}
$$

The two methods, key value multiples and traditional, use exactly the same principle, but the first method partitions into easy numbers, whereas the second method partitions according to place value.

The second method is often quicker, but only if you know all your multiplication facts. If you do not, or if you are not certain that you do, then the first method, although looking slightly longer, may in reality be quicker and more accurate.

There are some reasons why the 'traditional' method may be difficult for some learners:

- You have to know all the basic times/multiplication facts
- The layout is abstract. It does not self-explain
- The place values in each partial multiplication are more prone to error, for example, some people forget the 0 in 2610
- There is no built-in estimate

WORKSHEET M10

Use the 'traditional' method to calculate:

1)   35 x 47   2)   48 x 49   3)   67 x 82

4)   52 x 78   5)   135 x 213   6)   387 x 607

The special case of multiplying by 10, 100, 1000

This is a key skill and requires an understanding of place value.
A summary explanation is given below.

In order to understand how to multiply by 10, 100, 100 and other
multiples of 10 you have to understand place value.

Place value begins with and focuses on the unit.

Place value is then organised in multiples of 10 and divisors of 10,
for example:

     in 523

Start with the unit place value, the 3 represents 3 units, that is 3.

     the 2 represents 2 lots of ten, that is 2 units x 10, that is 20.

     the 5 represents 5 lots of 100, that is 5 units x 100, that is 500.

For decimals, place value is organised in divisors of 10,
for example:

     in 1.874

     the 8 represents 8 tenths of a unit, that is 8/10, 8 divided by 10.

     the 7 represents 7 hundredths of a unit, that is 7/100, 7 divided
     by 100.

     the 4 represents 4 thousandths of a unit, that is 4/1000, 4
     divided by 1000.

So, in the number   4444.444   each 4 has a different value; each
value of 4 is related to the next one by the power of 10.

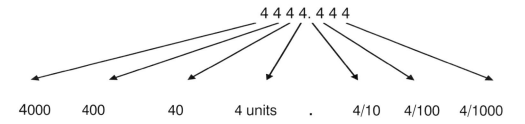

4000   400   40   4 units   .   4/10   4/100   4/1000

The decimal point identifies the unit place. Powers of 10 and divisors of 10 are symmetrical around the units place. So, to the left of 4 units is 4 tens and to the right of 4 units is 4 tenths.

Progress upwards one place value means a new place value which is 10x bigger. For example,

In the number below, the 4 in the tens place value is now printed in a bigger font:

4444.444

This 4 is 4 tens or 40.

The next higher place value is the hundreds, printed in a bigger font below,

4444.444

This 4 is 4 hundreds or 400, which is 10 x 40.

Each place value increases to the left by x 10.

Each place value decreases to the right by ÷ 10

The place value headings are:
1000   100   10   1 . 1/10   1/100   1/1000

WORKSHEET M11

Chose from place values   1000   100   10   1   1/10   1/100
and 1/1000 for the following questions. The first one is done as an
example.

1) 9**3**75.6   The 3 is 300, place value is hundreds, 100

2) 9375.**6**   The 6 is

3) 100**5**.92   The 5 is

4) 1005.**92**   The 9 is

5)   213.74**8**   The 8 is

6) 5316.72**9**   The 9 is

Look at the patterns in these examples of multiplying whole numbers
by 10, 100 and 1000:

5 x 1 = 5   5 x 10 = 50   5 x 100 = 500   5 x 1000 = 5000

50 x 1 = 50   50 x 10 = 500   50 x 100 = 5000   50 x 1000 = 50 000

500 x 1 = 500 500 x 100 = 5000 500 x 100 = 50 000 500 x 1000 = 500 000

Look at the patterns in these examples of multiplying decimal numbers
by 10, 100 and 1000. Focus on how the place value of the 4 changes.

0.4 x 1 = 0.4   0.4 x 10 = 4   0.4 x 100 = 40   0.4 x 1000 = 400

0.04 x 1 = 0.04   0.04 x 10 = 0.4   0.04 x 100 = 4   0.04 x 1000 = 40

0.004 x 1 = 0.004   0.004 x 10 = 0.04   0.004x 100 = 0.4   0.004 x 1000 = 4

In this 0.4 set of examples it may help if you focus on the 4 and its
place value. For example, in 0.004 x 1000, focus on the 4, which is
4/1000. If you multiply 4/1000 by 1000, the answer is 4.

The same pattern, of course, occurs with other numbers, for example,

$$1.234 \times 1 = 1.234 \qquad 1.234 \times 10 = 12.34$$
$$1.234 \times 100 = 123.4 \qquad 1.234 \times 1000 = 1234$$

Focus on the 1 and its place value which becomes ten, then a hundred and finally a thousand.

When you multiply a number by 1, one unit, the number stays the same value and the digits which make up the number stay in the same sequence and have the same value.

$$\text{For example:} \qquad 54321 \times 1 = 54321$$

When you multiply a number by 10, one ten, the number becomes 10x bigger.
The digits that make up the number stay in the same sequence, but each digit represents a number which is now 10x bigger than before it was multiplied.

$$54321 \times 10 = 543210$$

This rule could be demonstrated with base 10 materials or with money.

$$23 \times 10 = 230$$

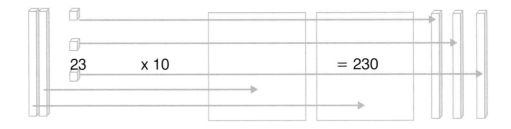

WORKSHEET M12

1) Multiply these numbers by 10.

    34   570   67.1   82.39   0.3

2) Multiply these numbers by 100.

    72   400   85.3   72.05   0.06

3) Multiply these numbers by 1000.

    18   310   59.9   1.804   0.008

4) Divide these numbers by 10.

    43   740   81.9   0.78

5) Divide these numbers by 100.

    64   850   94.5   1.74   0.25

6) Divide these numbers by 1000.

    48   620   38.2   8.03   0.16

Multiplication with decimal numbers

First we shall look at decimal numbers which are greater than 1, then at decimal numbers which are less than 1.

Multiplication by decimal numbers greater than 1

The main change will be in setting up the table of key values, which will now include some decimal values. For example,

$$345 \times 12.7$$

Hint: Set up the whole number values first:

1x	345 =	345
2x	345 =	690
5x	345 =	1725
10x	345 =	3450

Hint: Then set up the decimals starting with 0.1:

0.1x 345 = 34.5   *Hint:* This is the x1 value divided by 10.

0.2x 345 = 69.0   *Hint:* This is the x2 value (690) divided by 10 (also 2x the 0.1 value).

0.5x 345 = 172.5   *Hint:* This is half of the x1 value, that is 345 ÷ 2.

Break down, or partition, the 12.7 into   10 + 2 + 0.5 + 0.2

10	x 345	3450
2	x 345	690
0.5	x 345	172.5
0.2	x 345	69
12.7	x 345	4381.5

$$12.7 \times 345 = 4381.5$$

WORKSHEET M13

$$
\begin{array}{rclcr}
0.5 & \times & 345 & = & 172.5 \\
0.2 & \times & 345 & = & 69.0 \\
0.1 & \times & 345 & = & 34.5 \\
1 & \times & 345 & = & 345 \\
2 & \times & 345 & = & 690 \\
5 & \times & 345 & = & 1725 \\
10 & \times & 345 & = & 3450 \\
20 & \times & 345 & = & 6900 \\
\end{array}
$$

Use the key values table above to answer these questions:

1)   345 x 15.2   2)   345 x 20.3   3)   345 x 7.7

4)   345 x 30.4   5)   345 x 17.6   6)   345 x 10.8

WORKSHEET M14

Complete these key value tables.

1 x 27 =	1 x 105 =	1 x 83 =
0.1 x 27 = 2.7	0.1 x 105 =	0.1 x 83 =
0.2 x 27 =	0.2 x 105 =	0.2 x 83 =
0.5 x 27 =	0.5 x 105 =	0.5 x 83 =

Multiplication with decimal numbers less than 1

Some people think that multiplication always results in a bigger number. This is only true if the multiplying number is bigger than 1.

In this book 'bigger' is used to mean bigger in numerical value and so 'smaller' is used to mean smaller in numerical value.

If the multiplying number is less than 1 then the resulting answer will be smaller. For example,

$$0.1 \times 60 = 6$$

It may help you to understand this if you read 0.1 as 'one tenth'.

One tenth of 60 is six.

#	#	#	#	#	#

This rule applies even if the number being multiplied is also less than 1, for example:

$$0.5 \quad \times \quad 0.2 \quad = \quad 0.1$$

one half x two tenths = one tenth

The answer is smaller than either of the multiplying numbers. Since both multiplying numbers are less than 1, they each make the other number smaller!

For further evidence of this effect, look at this sequence, focusing on the multiplying number and the answers:

```
100     x 12 =   1200
 10     x 12 =    120
  1     x 12 =     12
  0.1   x 12 =      1.2      one tenth of 12
  0.01  x 12 =      0.12     one hundredth of 12
```

Note: To make this sequence clear, I have, as often elsewhere in this book, lined up (vertically) the place values of the numbers involved.

WORKSHEET M15

Use these key value multipliers to answer the questions below:

1	x	23	=	23		1	x	42	=	42
0.5	x	23	=	11.5		0.5	x	42	=	21
0.2	x	23	=	4.6		0.5	x	42	=	8.4
0.1	x	23	=	2.3		0.1	x	42	=	4.2
0.05	x	23	=	1.15		0.05	x	42	=	2.1
						0.02	x	42	=	0.84
						0.01	x	42	=	0.42

Example: 23 x 0.6

0.6 breaks down into 0.5 + 0.1

$$
\begin{array}{rl}
0.5 \text{ x } 23 = & 11.5 \\
0.1 \text{ x } 23 = & \underline{2.3} \\
0.6 \text{ x } 23 = & 13.8
\end{array}
$$

1)   23 x 0.7

2)   23 x 0.15

3)   23 x 0.65

4)   42 x 0.21

5)   42 x 0.62

6)   42 x 0.08

Summary

There are some reasons why the 'traditional' methods of multiplication may be difficult for some learners:

- You have to know all the basic times/multiplication facts

- The layout is abstract. It does not self-explain

- The layout requires good spatial skills when writing

- There is no built-in estimate

For more practice and support on parts of number, please see, *What to do when you can't do fractions, decimals and percentages.*

Section

2

DIVISION

DIVISION

This section of the book looks at and addresses some of the reasons learners may get confused about division.

The reasons include:

- Confusing language
- The order/sequence of working with the standard procedures
- A weak understanding of what division means
- A weak understanding of what the traditional division procedures/ methods mean
- A limited recall/retrieval of basic facts
- The order in which the numbers are written in a problem is not always the order in which they are computed
- Inability to check or appraise answers
- Fear of failure

Each 'What to do…' book is a part of a structure that makes maths skills more accessible.

This is achieved by:

- Using number facts that most people can recall/retrieve
- Introducing understandable ways to tackle maths
- Linking these ways so that each way supports and develops old and new skills

Division is often considered by learners to be the hardest of the four operations on numbers.

The four operations are addition, subtraction, multiplication and division and are called 'operations' because they are how we work on, or operate on, numbers.

- For addition we are putting numbers together
- For subtraction we are separating numbers
- For multiplication we are combining or adding several of the same number
- For division we are taking away several of the same number in order to divide or separate it into a number of equal parts

Let's look at some examples:

Addition

Addition is a sub-skill of division. The following activities offer a brief review of this skill. For a more detailed explanation see 'What to do when you can't add and subtract'.

10 add 15. 10 + 1. We put together, or add, 10 and 15 to get 25.

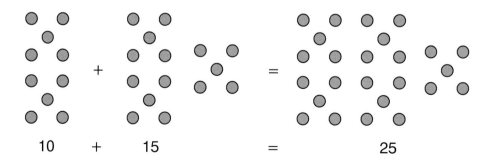

ACTIVITY D1 (see also ACTIVITY M1)
Practising addition. The pattern of adding 10.

1.   Start with ten coins or counters set out in the five pattern.
        Write 10 + next to them.

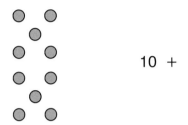

10 +

Now set out 1 coin (or counter) next to the ten coins and write 1 as
shown:

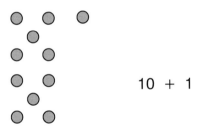

10 + 1

Count the coins (counters) and write the total: ....
Check that the answer is correct.
If not, try re-counting, starting after 10.

Note: Although the digits used follow a logical pattern, the words
used for the first two digit numbers, 11 (eleven) and 12 (twelve), do
not follow a logical pattern of language. Eleven and twelve are one-off
exceptions before the teen numbers start their somewhat confusing
pattern. The pattern is confusing because the unit digit is spoken
before the ten digit, for example we write 14, yet we say fourteen as
"four ten".

Now, to set up the next example, remove the group of 1 coin (counter) and replace it with 2 coins (counters) so that you have 10 + 2.

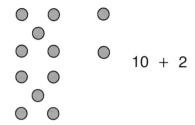 10 + 2

Write the total number of coins (counters): ....
Check that your answer is correct. If not ask for assistance.

Repeat this activity for 10 + 3 onwards.

10 + 1	11
10 + 2	12
10 + 3	....
10 + 4	....
10 + 5	....
10 + 6	....
10 + 7	....
10 + 8	....
10 + 9	....

Can you see a pattern in the numbers in your answers?

How would that pattern change and what would the answers be if you were adding onto 11 instead of 10?

11 + 2   ....
11 + 3   ....
11 + 4   ....
11 + 5   ....
11 + 6   ....
11 + 7   ....
11 + 8   ....
11 + 9   ....

Make sure you use coins, setting them out as for the last example, using the fives patterns, even if you have felt confident enough not to use them for the previous examples.

Now, look at the pattern when you add onto 9. Compare it to the patterns of adding onto 10 and onto 11.

9 + 2   ....
9 + 3   ....
9 + 4   ....
9 + 5   ....
9 + 6   ....
9 + 7   ....
9 + 8   ....
9 + 9   ....

You can use coins to show how this 9+ pattern develops from the 10+ pattern.

If you set up the coins to show 9 + 4, then move one coin from the 4 to make the 9 up to 10, this changes the addition into 10 + 3.

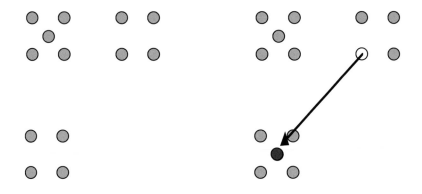

ACTIVITY D2 Adding with 'carrying' or 'trading'. e.g. 47 + 17

The next activities use 10p and 1p coins to demonstrate place value issues.

The first activity in this part demonstrates the need to 'trade' (or 'carry') ten 1p coins for one 10p coin.

Set up 47 and 17.

Now add them together.

$$7 \quad + \quad 7 \quad = \quad 14 \quad \text{and}$$
$$40 \quad + \quad 10 \quad = \quad 50$$

Trade ten 1p coins for one 10p coin.

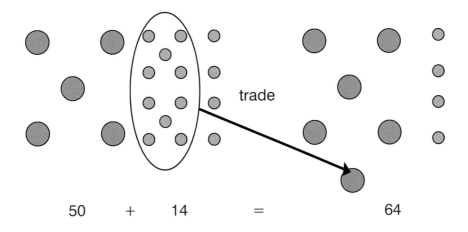

trade

50   +   14   =   64

Set up other examples for the learner.

If the learner is not able to do these successfully, then return to the programme in 'What to do when you can't add and subtract.'

WORKSHEET D1 Addition

1) 46 + 10 =   2) 46 + 9 =   3) 46 + 8 =

4) 54 + 6 =   5) 56 + 4 =   6) 56 + 5 =

7) 78 + 8 =   8) 37 + 7 =   9) 66 + 6 =

10) 28 + 18 =   11) 37 + 17 =   12) 46 +16 =

13)   74   14)   46   15)   77
        +22   +38   +17

16)   212   17)   307   18)   526
       +334   +284   +286

Note: The questions are set to explore patterns and to be diagnostic of addition errors. Should a learner achieve a low score, then Worksheet D2 can be used as a post-intervention check). If the learner is not able to do these second examples successfully, then return to the programme in 'What to do when you can't add and subtract.' Addition is a pre-requisite skill for some division procedures.

WORKSHEET D2 Addition

1) 76 + 10 =

2) 76 + 9 =

3) 76 + 8 =

4) 43 + 7 =

5) 47 + 3 =

6) 47 + 4 =

7) 18 + 8 =

8) 27 + 7 =

9) 46 + 6 =

10) 38 + 28 =

11) 57 + 27 =

12) 26 + 26 =

13)
```
    41
   +17
```

14)
```
    56
   +38
```

15)
```
    73
   +19
```

16)
```
   322
  +143
```

17)
```
   409
  +262
```

18)
```
   578
  +334
```

Subtraction: Subtraction is a key sub-skill for division. The next activities offer a brief review of this skill.

For a comprehensive explanation of subtraction see 'What to do when you can't add and subtract'.

30 subtract 20. 30 – 20. We start with 30 and take away 20 to get 10.

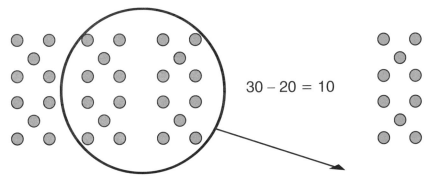

30 – 20 = 10

Note: For addition you put together and for subtraction you separate. They are related by being opposite operations.

53

ACTIVITY D3

Set up 40 coins in the fives pattern. Then subtract (by taking away) 30.
Write 40 − 30 = 10.

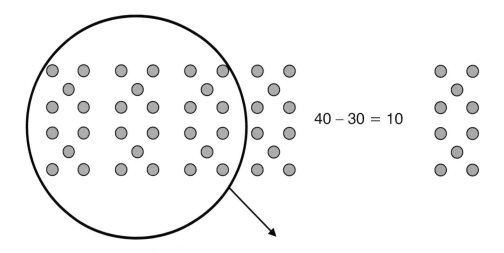

40 − 30 = 10

Set up other examples, such as 35 − 6, each time writing the number
sentence as you move the coins. Discuss the vocabulary, 'take away,
separate, subtract'.

ACTIVITY D4

We start the next activity using only 1p coins. These activities look at subtraction as 'taking away' and as counting back and then by counting on.

The first activity uses coins to work out 13 – 6. Set up 13 coins using the 'five' pattern. Then take away 6 coins (shaded black in the second diagram). The answer, 7, could be obtained by counting back from 13 and the layout of the coins could be used to demonstrate that strategy.

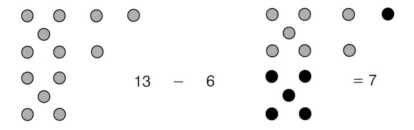

The diagram/layout below could be used to show how counting on from 6 to 13 would also give an answer of 7. It also demonstrates why the counting on begins at the number following 6, that is, 7. The black counters only are counted.

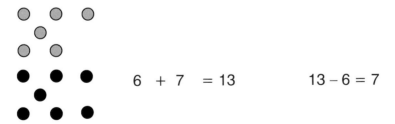

Set up another similar example and check if the learner can do the activities correctly.

The next activities use 10p and 1p coins to demonstrate place value issues.

The first activity in this part demonstrates the need to 'trade' (or 'decompose' or 'rename') one 10p into ten 1p coins.

Set up 34, ready for the subtraction of 16.   34 – 16.

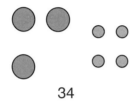

34

Discuss with the learner how six 1p coins cannot be subtracted/taken away when there are only four 1p coins. Show how trading one of the 10p coins can generate an extra ten 1p coins whilst still leaving the total value as 34p.

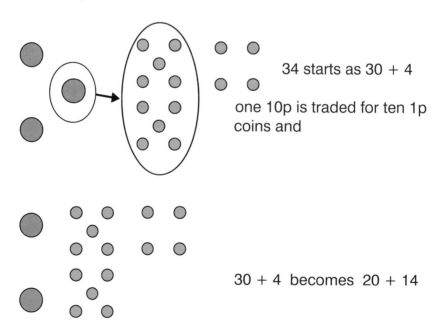

34 starts as 30 + 4

one 10p is traded for ten 1p coins and

30 + 4 becomes 20 + 14

Now take away 16p as one 10p and six 1p coins (shaded black), leaving 18p.

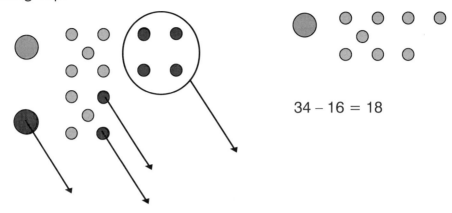

$$34 - 16 = 18$$

Show how this is written in vertical form.

$$\begin{array}{r} {}^2\cancel{3}{}^1 4 \\ -\ 1\ 6 \\ \hline 1\ 8 \end{array}$$

It may help some learners to use an intermediate line and place value columns to show the trading more explicitly:

Tens	Units	
3	4	
2	14	2 tens (10p) and 14 units (1p)
− 1	6	
1	8	

Set up 56 and ask the learner to take away 27 by using trading. Show how this is written out.

If the learner is not able to do this successfully, then return to the programme in *'What to do when you can't add and subtract'.*

Note: Subtraction is an essential sub-skill for division.

WORKSHEET D4

1)　8 − 7 =

2)　18 − 7 =

3)　68 − 27 =

4)　16 − 9 =

5)　26 − 9 =

6)　36 − 19 =

7)　　 68
　　− 37

8)　　 68
　　− 38

9)　　 68
　　− 39

10)　　 88
　　− 28

11)　　 89
　　− 28

12)　　 90
　　− 28

13)　　 853
　　− 637

14)　　 715
　　− 543

15)　　 237
　　− 138

16)　　 460
　　− 128

17)　　 702
　　− 361

18)　　 600
　　− 173

Worksheet D4 is provided for a post-intervention check.

WORKSHEET D5

1) $7 - 6 =$

2) $17 - 6 =$

3) $67 - 26 =$

4) $14 - 9 =$

5) $24 - 9 =$

6) $34 - 19 =$

7) $\begin{array}{r} 67 \\ -\ 47 \\ \hline \end{array}$

8) $\begin{array}{r} 67 \\ -\ 48 \\ \hline \end{array}$

9) $\begin{array}{r} 67 \\ -\ 49 \\ \hline \end{array}$

10) $\begin{array}{r} 68 \\ -\ 18 \\ \hline \end{array}$

11) $\begin{array}{r} 69 \\ -\ 18 \\ \hline \end{array}$

12) $\begin{array}{r} 70 \\ -\ 18 \\ \hline \end{array}$

13) $\begin{array}{r} 874 \\ -\ 326 \\ \hline \end{array}$

14) $\begin{array}{r} 626 \\ -\ 283 \\ \hline \end{array}$

15) $\begin{array}{r} 443 \\ -\ 244 \\ \hline \end{array}$

16) $\begin{array}{r} 380 \\ -\ 127 \\ \hline \end{array}$

17) $\begin{array}{r} 804 \\ -\ 432 \\ \hline \end{array}$

18) $\begin{array}{r} 800 \\ -\ 287 \\ \hline \end{array}$

Subtraction skills are covered in more detail in *'What to do when you can't add and subtract'*.

Multiplication   6 times 10. 6 x 10. We add 6 lots of 10 to get 60.

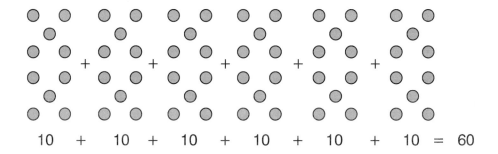

10   +   10   +   10   +   10   +   10   +   10   =   60

Multiplication is related to addition, so our 6 x 10 is actually 10 + 10 + 10 + 10 + 10 + 10, that is 6 additions of 10. Multiplication can also be 'seen' as the opposite of division.

When we use 'lots of' to infer multiplication we are inferring repeated addition.

ACTIVITY D5

Set up several examples of 'lots of' coins to demonstrate repeated addition, for example:

4   +   4   +   4   +   4   = 16

For more practice and support in working with the times tables, see *'What to do when you can't learn the times tables'*.

Division and the times table facts

Division is the opposite operation to multiplication. Basic multiplication facts, the times tables can illustrate this:

Times table fact: $7 \times 4 = 28$
Division fact: $28 \div 7 = 4$

Times table fact: $8 \times 6 = 48$
Division fact: $48 \div 8 = 6$

The times table square can also be used for division:

For example, $48 \div 6 = 8$

Find 48 in the square by tracking down the 6 column.

	0	1	2	3	4	5	6	7	8	9	10
0	0	0	0	0	0	0	0	0	0	0	0
1	0	1	2	3	4	5	6	7	8	9	10
2	0	2	4	6	8	10	12	14	16	18	20
3	0	3	6	9	12	15	18	21	24	27	30
4	0	4	8	12	16	20	24	28	32	36	40
5	0	5	10	15	20	25	30	35	40	45	50
6	0	6	12	18	24	30	36	42	48	54	60
7	0	7	14	21	28	35	42	49	56	63	70
8	0	8	16	24	32	40	**48**	56	64	72	80
9	0	9	18	27	6	45	54	63	72	81	90
10	0	10	20	30	40	50	60	70	80	90	100

Now track across to find the answer, 8.

	0	1	2	3	4	5	**6**	7	8	9	10
0	0	0	0	0	0	0	0	0	0	0	0
1	0	1	2	3	4	5	6	7	8	9	10
2	0	2	4	6	8	10	12	14	16	18	20
3	0	3	6	9	12	15	18	21	24	27	30
4	0	4	8	12	16	20	24	28	32	36	40
5	0	5	10	15	20	25	30	35	40	45	50
6	0	6	12	18	24	30	36	42	48	54	60
7	0	7	14	21	28	35	42	49	56	63	70
8	0	8	16	24	32	40	**48**	56	64	72	80
9	0	9	18	27	6	45	54	63	72	81	90
10	0	10	20	30	40	50	60	70	80	90	100

$$48 \div 6 = \quad 8$$

Division

We can now look at how 'division' itself can be understood.

For example: 50 divided by 5 $50 \div 5$

We have two ways of interpreting the maths language '50 divided by 5'

The first way, repeated subtraction:

We start with 50 objects and work out how many times we can take away 5 objects. This is sometimes said as 'how many fives in fifty?' This interpretation relates division as the opposite operation to multiplication.

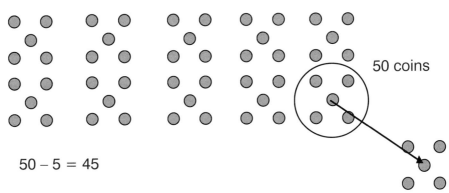

50 coins

$50 - 5 = 45$

1 lot of 5

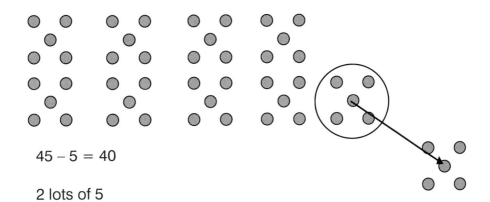

$45 - 5 = 40$

2 lots of 5

63

If we continue to subtract 5, then in numbers we have:

$$50 - 5 = 45$$
$$45 - 5 = 40$$
$$40 - 5 = 35$$
$$35 - 5 = 30$$
$$30 - 5 = 25$$
$$25 - 5 = 20$$
$$20 - 5 = 15$$
$$15 - 5 = 10$$
$$10 - 5 = 5$$
$$5 - 5 = 0$$

This is 10 repeated subtractions of 5, giving an answer of 10.

$$50 \div 5 = 10$$

Multiplication and division are opposites. If we look at and compare 10 x 5 and 50 ÷ 5, we can see that 10 x 5 is adding ten lots of 5 and that 50 ÷ 5 is subtracting 10 lots of 5.

10 x 5 is 10 repeated additions of 5.

$0 + 5 = 5$	
$5 + 5 = 10$	$50 - 5 = 45$
$10 + 5 = .15$	$45 - 5 = 40$
$15 + 5 = 20$	$40 - 5 = 35$
$20 + 5 = 25$	$35 - 5 = 30$
$25 + 5 = 30$	$30 - 5 = 25$
$30 + 5 = 35$	$25 - 5 = 20$
$35 + 5 = 40$	$20 - 5 = 15$
$40 + 5 = 45$	$15 - 5 = 10$
$45 + 5 = 50$	$10 - 5 = 5$
	$5 - 5 = 0$

50 ÷5 is 10 repeated subtractions of 5.

To sum up so far

Addition and multiplication are
about putting together

Subtraction and division are
about separating

Multiplication is about
repeatedly adding the same number

Division is about
repeatedly taking away the same number

ACTIVITY D6

1) Working out 72 ÷ 12 using coins and repeated subtraction.

Set out 72p in coins as shown, using six 10p coins and twelve 1p coins.

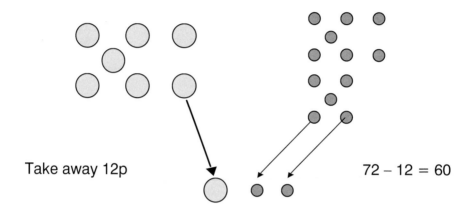

Take away 12p

72 – 12 = 60

Continue to take away 12p until all the coins have been used, writing the subtraction in numbers each time.

$$72 - 12 = 60$$
$$60 - 12 = 48$$
$$48 - 12 = 36$$
$$36 - 12 = 24$$
$$24 - 12 = 12$$
$$12 - 12 = 0$$

Count how many groups of 12p have been created. The number of groups is the answer to:

$$\textbf{72} \div \textbf{12} = \textbf{6}$$

2) Working out $104 \div 13$.

Set up a repeated subtraction, subtracting 13 until reaching 0, zero.

$$\begin{array}{r} 104 \\ -\ 13 \\ \hline 91 \end{array} \qquad \begin{array}{r} 91 \\ -\ 13 \\ \hline 78 \end{array} \qquad \begin{array}{r} 78 \\ -\ 13 \\ \hline \end{array}$$

How many subtractions do you need to do to reach zero?

A second word for division: sharing

When children are first introduced to division it is often explained in terms of 'sharing'. Sharing could also be described as 'dividing up into equal amounts'.

This is our second way of interpreting $50 \div 5$.

The change in wording creates a change in the explanation of division. 'Sharing and share' need to be understood for three reasons:

    1)   'Sharing' helps develop the concept of division.
    2)   Children (and adults) will meet this description and need to be flexible enough to move between the two interpretations.
    3)   There could easily be a misunderstanding if the different implications of these two words are not appreciated.

Ultimately, sharing means the same as repeated subtraction.

Let's explain what 'share' means and what makes it different and what makes it the same as 'divide' by an example that uses 40 and 5 again:

Start with 40 coins:

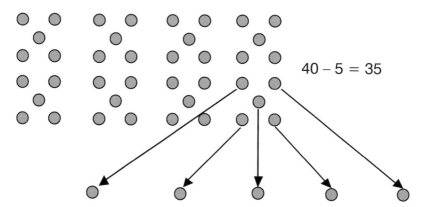

$40 - 5 = 35$

To share the 40 between 5 (places), we put one coin into each of the 5 places, leaving 35 coins.

We then put another coin into each of the 5 places:

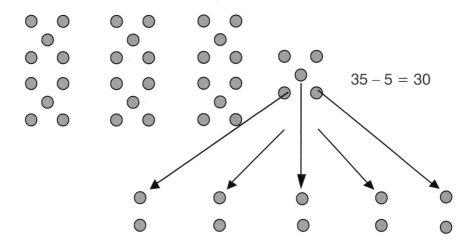

$35 - 5 = 30$

This procedure carries on until all of the coins are shared into the five places. There will then be 8 coins in each place, so sharing 40 coins equally between five places results in each pile having 8 coins.

'Sharing' implies 'equal shares'.

Another example:

If you share (equally) £50 between 5 people, how much does each person receive?

The picture for this is of 5 people in a line:

The £50 is shared out, £1 at a time, to each of the five people. So, in going down the line first time, each person receives £1 and £5 is used up or taken away from the £50.

In going down the line a second time, each person receives £1 and £10 is now used up or taken away from our starting amount.

In going down the line a third time, each person receives £1 and £15 is now used up or taken away from our starting amount.

In going down the line a fourth time, each person receives £1 and £20 is now used up or taken away from our starting amount

And so on until in going down the line a tenth time, each person receives £1 and all £50 is now used up or taken away from our starting amount.

Each person now has £10, so £50 has been shared equally between 5 people.

Summary: The process is, in effect, repeated subtraction, that is, repeatedly subtracting £5, but this time by sharing the £5 out as £1 at a time. So 'sharing' has the same outcome as 'dividing'. It separates the original quantity into five equal parts.

Division and multiplication are linked as opposite operations, but we have to remember that the order in which the numbers are multiplied makes no difference to the answer, both 5 x 10 and 10 x 5 equal 50. but the order of the numbers in division does make a difference to the answer:

So $50 \div 10 = 5$

whereas $50 \div 5 = 10$

$50 \div 10$ can be written in words as '50 divided by 10' or as 'how much do you get if you share 50 into 10 equal parts?' .The answer is 5.

$50 \div 5$ can be written in words as '50 divided by 5' or as 'how much do you get if you share 50 into 5 equal parts?' The answer is 10.

ACTIVITY D7

1) Set up 48 coins and share them equally between 12 places.

   Each place gets .... coins.

2) Set up 57 coins and share them equally between 3 places.

   Each place gets .... coins

The problem with order

The word 'into' is often connected with division. It can be confusing and we need to exercise great care when saying, writing or interpreting 'into'.

For example, we say 'five divided into fifty' yet we write this in symbols as a number sentence:

$$50 \div 5.$$

The numbers are spoken in the reverse order as that used in the number sentence.

Also, this spoken order of the words puts the numbers and symbols in the wrong order for entry into a calculator.

However, 'five divided into fifty' does have the same order as the presentation used for the standard computation method:

$$5\overline{)50}$$

'Five divided into fifty' could just as reasonably be interpreted as '5 divided into 50 parts', but that would be wrong. The correct interpretation is all in the emphasis put on the words and is a major contributor to confusion about division. The implication or the inclusion of the word 'parts' makes a radical change to the meaning.

'Five divided into 50' means that the 5 is doing the 'divided into' and the 50 is being divided or separated.

'Five divided into 50 parts' means that 5 is being divided or separated (into 50 parts). The extra word 'parts' completely changes the question. The 50 is doing the 'divided into' and the 5 is being divided (into 50 parts, parts that will be less than 1, in fact they will be 0.1).

We also use another phrasing (again, very similar to the other forms) for division and say, 'twenty divided by five' and write this in symbol and numbers as 20 ÷ 5. The numbers are spoken in the same order as that used in symbols. The word 'into' has not been used.

Another, somewhat abstract wording is 'how many fives in 20?'. If you asked a naïve person 'how many fives in 55?' they might respond, reasonably, 'two' instead of the maths response of 'eleven'.

'How many fives in twenty?' means 'how many fives can I take away from 20 to end up with zero?'

A second example:

The interpretation of 60 ÷ 5 into words for this method is 'How many times can I take away/subtract 5 from 60?' if it is to make sense. This is a less abstract question than, 'how many fives in sixty?' and can be demonstrated by using coins or objects.

ACTIVITY D8

Set out 60 coins, using the clusters of 5. It is then possible to see and to count 'how many fives in sixty?'

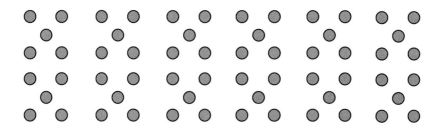

Note: Before starting any division calculation, it is critical that the numbers and symbols are in the right order. If they are not computed in the right order the answer will be wrong. Although the individual words used in the examples above are simple, the order in which they are used can change the mathematical meaning.

ACTIVITY D9

For this activity you need a calculator. Use the calculator to find the answer for each question. Be careful about the order in which you enter the numbers and the ÷ symbol. Write down the order you use for the numbers and the ÷ symbol. Check your answer each time.

1) 70 ÷ 5   *(14)*   2) Divide 84 by 4   *(21)*

3) Divide 7 into 84   *(12)*   4) Divide 9 into 153   *(17)*

5) Divide 28 into 7 equal parts   *(4)*

6) Divide 5 into 10 equal parts   *(0.5)*

7) 7 divided into 105   *(15)*   8) 144 divided by 12   *(12)*

9) 12 divided into 6   *(0.5)*   10) 6 divided by 12   *(0.5)*

Relating division to multiplication (be careful with order)

This concept was introduced at the start of the work on division on page 46.

The basic multiplication facts are not dependent on order, for example:

$$4 \times 7 = 28 \quad \text{and} \quad 7 \times 4 = 28$$

Multiplying 4 by 7 gives the same answer as multiplying 7 by 4.

Division facts are dependent on order. Dividing 28 by 7 gives a different answer to dividing 7 by 28

$$28 \div 7 = 4 \qquad 7 \div 28 = 0.25$$

Factors

In the example above we used $\qquad 7 \times 4 = 28$

which could be turned around to read $\qquad 28 = 7 \times 4$

7 and 4 are called **factors**.

A factor is a number that divides into another number.
Each multiplication fact tells you two factors of the answer number.

For example:

if you know that $9 \times 6 = 54$

then you know that 6 and 9 are factors of 54.

Quicker sharing

In the £50 sharing example above we were still taking away £5 from our starting amount of £50 each time we went down the line of people.

We went down the line 10 times, each time sharing out as £1 to each person and therefore using up £5, so this was, again, repeated subtraction from the starting amount.

We could shorten the sharing process a little by giving out £2 to each person, then another £2 then another £2 and so on until the £50 is used up. This means we would each time take away £10 from our £50, then take away another £10 and then take away another £10 and so on from the original £50. We would have done 5 sharings instead of ten, but each sharing gave out twice as much.

Repeated subtraction does not have to be done in one lot at a time. It can be done in groups or 'chunks' or multiples.

It is a long, and inefficient process to share one at a time.

We can group in 'easy' chunks/multiples and thus take away several at one time. In the example above, we take away two each time to share. This combines two fives to make ten.

$$2 \times 5 = 10$$

Then take away tens from 50, with each subtraction of 10 being a subtraction of 2 x 5, two lots of 5:

$$50 - 10 = 40$$
$$40 - 10 = 30$$
$$30 - 10 = 20$$
$$20 - 10 = 10$$
$$10 - 10 = \ 0$$

We have taken away (subtracted) five tens. As each 10 is two lots of 5, we have subtracted $5 \times 2 = 10$ fives.

For big numbers divided by 5 we could take away groups of 10 fives.

$$10 \times 5 = 50$$

(We could have done our example above in one go by using ten fives.)

For even bigger numbers divided by 5 we could take away groups of 20 or 50 or 100 fives.

$$20 \times 5 = 100$$
$$50 \times 5 = 250$$
$$100 \times 5 = 500$$

A second example, £60 shared equally between 5 people: $60 \div 5$

As with the previous method, we could shorten the process a little by giving out £2 to each person, then £2 then £2 and so on to each person. This means we would have taken £10, then £10 and then £10 away and so on from the £60. Repeated subtraction does not have to be done in one lot at a time. It can be done in groups or 'chunks'. The chunks could be bigger than 2 lots.

If we subtract just 5 each time until we reached 0, it would take 12 subtractions.

Or we could use some easy multiples of 5, for example:

$$2 \times 5 = 10 \qquad \text{'2 lots of 5'}$$
$$10 \times 5 = 50 \qquad \text{'10 lots of 5'}$$

We then need only two subtractions:

$$60 - 50 = 10 \qquad (\textbf{10} \text{ lots of 5})$$
$$10 - 10 = 0 \qquad (\ \textbf{2} \text{ lots of 5})$$

To get an answer we add together the 10 'lots of' and the 2 'lots of'.

'**10** lots of 5' plus '**2** lots of 5' = '**12** lots of 5'

$$60 \div 5 = 12$$

So, in this method for 60 ÷ 5 the focus is again on the repeated subtraction of 5 or groups of 5.

Note: Division requires an ability to subtract. If you do not have this skill, then refer to *'What to do when you can't add and subtract'*

Division with bigger numbers

This requires the setting up a table of key value (easy) multiples.

If we want to make the repeated subtraction quicker and more efficient, which will be necessary for bigger numbers, we can subtract in multiples or chunks.

For our first example we will use 15 again to illustrate the principle:

$$390 \div 15$$

The table of key value multiples of 15 looks like this:

$$1 \times 15 = 15$$
$$2 \times 15 = 30$$
$$5 \times 15 = 75$$
$$10 \times 15 = 150$$
$$20 \times 15 = 300$$
$$50 \times 15 = 750$$

There is a pattern in this table. Compare the answers for 1 x 15 and 10 x 15 and 2 x 15 and 20 x 15 and the answers for 5 x 15 and 50 x 15.

This gives you a check on the answers for the key value multiples.

For example,

a division fact is $\qquad$ $750 \div 15 = 50$
and the related multiplication fact is $\qquad$ $50 \times 15 = 750$

We can look at the table of key value multiples and estimate an answer to the division. In our example,

$$390 \div 15 = ?$$
the related multiplication fact is $\qquad$ $? \times 15 = 390$

The closest values to 390 from the table are:

$$20 \times 15 = 300 \quad \text{and}$$
$$50 \times 15 = 750$$

390 is between 300 and 750, so our answer must be between 20 and 50, and closer to 20 than 50.

Note: This method is linking division to multiplication. Constructing the table of key value multiples makes this link. It enables you to make an estimate of the final answer.

Division by subtraction of key value multiples

Now do the subtraction of multiples or 'chunks' of 15.

$$
\begin{array}{r}
390 \\
-\ 300 \\
\hline
90 \\
-\ 75 \\
\hline
15 \\
-\ 15 \\
\hline
0
\end{array}
\qquad
\begin{array}{l}
20 \quad \text{(20 lots of 15)} \\[1.2em]
5 \quad \text{(5 lots of 15)} \\[1.2em]
1 \quad \text{(1 lot of 15)}
\end{array}
$$

We have subtracted   **20 + 5 + 1** lots of 15.

So the answer is   **20 + 5 + 1** = 26

$$390 \div 15 = 26$$

This method is based on the same principle as the traditional method for 'long' division, which also uses subtraction of multiples, but does not use key multiples.

WORKSHEET D4

Use the table of key value multiples to work out estimates of the answers for the questions below:

$$1 \quad x\,6 = \quad 6$$
$$2 \quad x\,6 = \quad 12$$
$$5 \quad x\,6 = \quad 30$$
$$10 \quad x\,6 = \quad 60$$
$$20 \quad x\,6 = \quad 120$$
$$50 \quad x\,6 = \quad 240$$
$$100 \quad x\,6 = \quad 600$$

1) $306 \div 6$ Hint: $(? \times 6 = 306)$ 2) $132 \div 6$ Hint: $(? \times 6 = 132)$

3) $186 \div 6$ Hint: $(? \times 6 = 186)$ 4) $294 \div 6$

5) $732 \div 6$ 6) $912 \div 6$

WORKSHEET D5

Use the table of key value multiples to work out the exact answers for these questions:

$$1 \quad x\,6 = \quad 6$$
$$2 \quad x\,6 = \quad 12$$
$$5 \quad x\,6 = \quad 30$$
$$10 \quad x\,6 = \quad 60$$
$$20 \quad x\,6 = \quad 120$$
$$50 \quad x\,6 = \quad 240$$
$$101 \quad x\,6 = \quad 600$$

1) $306 \div 6$ 2) $132 \div 6$ 3) $186 \div 6$

4) $294 \div 6$ 5) $732 \div 6$ 6) $912 \div 6$

Division by 2 digit numbers

The principle is the same as explained above, when we divided by a one digit number. The first step is to set up a table of key multiples.

For example, to compute the division, 1139 ÷ 17

1 x 17 =	17	
2 x 17 =	34	
5 x 17 =	85	
10 x 17 =	170	*(Hint: To check 5 x 17, divide the answer to 10 x 17 by 2)*
20 x 17 =	340	*(Hint: To check 20 x 17, look at 2 x 17. 34 has become 340)*
50 x 17 =	850	*(Hint: To check 50 x 17, look at 5 x 17. 85 has become 850)*
100 x 17 =	1700	

We can now make an estimate of the answer:

100 x 17 gives a value 1700, which is greater than 1139,
50 x 17 gives a value 850, which is smaller than 1139.
This means that the answer to our division must lie between 50 and 100.

The table of key value multiples can always be used in this way to estimate an answer to any division.

Now subtract the key values from 1139.

```
     1139
 −    850        50  x 17
      289
 −    170        10  x 17
      119
 −     85         5  x 17
       34
 −     34         2  x 17
        0
```

Now add up the key value multipliers (which are in bold print).

$$50 + 10 + 5 + 2 \ = \ 67$$

So the answer is 67: $1139 \div 17 = 67$

WORKSHEET D6 Setting up key value tables.

Example: Setting up a key value multipliers table for 23:

$$
\begin{array}{rrr}
23 \ \text{x} & 1 & = & 23 \\
23 \ \text{x} & 2 & = & 46 \\
23 \ \text{x} & 5 & = & 115 \\
23 \ \text{x} & 10 & = & 230 \\
23 \ \text{x} & 20 & = & 460 \\
23 \ \text{x} & 50 & = & 1150 \\
23 \ \text{x} & 100 & = & 2300 \\
\end{array}
$$

Remember to do the checks by looking at related values. In this 23 example it could be by comparing,

23 x 2 and 23 x 20   or   23 x 10 and 23 x 5

Set up tables of key value multipliers:

1)
31 x   1   =   31
31 x   2   =
31 x   5   =
31 x   10   =
31 x   20   = 620
31 x   50   =
31 x 100   =

2)
43 x   1   =
43 x   2   =
43 x   5   = 215
43 x   10   =
43 x   20   =
43 x   50   =
43 x 100   =

*** Make sure that questions 1 and 2 are correct before you carry on ***

WORKSHEET D6 (continued)

Set up tables of key value multipliers to 100 for these questions:

3)   41   4)   17

5)   53   6)   61

WORKSHEET D7

Use the key values tables from WORKSHEET D 6 to work out the answers to these questions.

For each question make an estimate first.

1) $1302 \div 31$ 2) $3416 \div 61$

*** Make sure you have checked that questions 1) and 2) are correct before you move on to questions 3) to 6) ***

3) $391 \div 23$ 4) $1376 \div 43$

5) $3975 \div 53$ 6) $2501 \div 61$

The special case of dividing by 10, 100, 1000

In order to understand how to divide by 10, 100, 1000 and other multiples of 10 you have to understand place value.

Place value is organised in multiples of 10, centred on 'units'.

For example:

in 523:

the 3 represents 3 units (1), that is 3

the 2 represents 2 lots of 10, that is 20

the 5 represents 5 lots of 100, that is 500

For decimals, place value is organised in divisors of 10, centred on 'units' (1/10, 1/100, 1/1000) for example:

in 1.874:

the 8 represents 8 tenths of a unit, that is 8/10

the 7 represents 7 hundredths of a unit, that is 8/100

the 4 represents 4 thousandths of a unit, that is 4/1000

So, in the number 4444.444 each 4 has a different value. Each value is related to 4 units by a multiple or divisor of 10.

4444.444

4000	400	40	4 units.	4/10	4/100	4/1000
4 thousands	4 hundreds	4 tens		4 tenths	4 hundredths	4 thousandths

The decimal point identifies the unit place. Powers of 10 and divisors of 10 are symmetrical around the units place. So, for example, to the left of 4 units is 4 tens and to the right of 4 units is 4 tenths.

Progress upwards one place value, means a new place value which is 10x bigger.

In our 4444.444, for example 40 x 10 = 400   40 becomes 400

$$4444.444 \text{ x } 10 = 44444.44$$

←———————————————

$$4444.444 \div 10 = 444.4444$$

———————————————→

Progress downwards one place value, means a new place value which has been divided by 10,

For example, $0.4 \div 10 = 0.04$

4/10 becomes 4/100

$$4444.444 \div 10 = 444.4444$$

Patterns

Look at the patterns in these examples of dividing by 1, 10, 100 and 1000:

5000	÷	1	= 5000	5000	÷	10	= 500
5000	÷	100	= 50	5000	÷	1000	= 5

500	÷	1	= 500	500	÷	10	= 50
500	÷	100	= 5	500	÷	1000	= 0.5

50	÷	1	= 50	50	÷	10	= 5
50	÷	100	= 0.5	50	÷	1000	= 0.05

1234	÷	1	= 1234	1234	÷	10	= 123.4
1234	÷	100	= 12.34	1234	÷	1000	= 1.234

123.4	÷	1	= 123.4	123.4	÷	10	= 12.34
123.4	÷	100	= 1.234	123.4	÷	1000	= 0.1234

12.34	÷	1	= 12.34	12.34	÷	10	= 1.234
12.34	÷	100	= 0.1234	12.34	÷	1000	= 0.01234

In this second set of examples it may help if you focus on one of the digits and its place value.

For example, in 123.4 ÷ 100, focus on the digit 1, which here represents 100. If you divide 100 by 100, the answer is 1. The other digits follow 1 in the original sequence.

So 123.4 becomes 1.234

WORKSHEET D8

1) Divide these numbers by 1.

   7   83   105   9758   0.75

2) Divide these numbers by 10.

   57   680   93.6   7.25   0.28

3) Divide these numbers by 100.

   82   480   27.3   2.03   0.15

4) Divide these numbers by 1000.

   36   460   27.1   9.12   2.3

Division and decimals

Until we reached the section on dividing by 10, 100, 100 etc, our division answers have always been whole numbers. This is not always the case.

For example: **26 ÷ 5**

To deal with this we have to extend our key value multiples table to include decimals.

If you are not sure about this, check *'What to do when you can't do fractions, decimals and percentages'*.

There is still a pattern in these new key value multiples.

Start with 1 x 5.

1 x 5 = 5	1 x 5 = 5
0.5 x 5 = 2.5	2 x 5 = 10
0.2 x 5 = 1.0	5 x 5 = 25
0.1 x 5 = 0.5	10 x 5 = 50

Now subtract the key value multiples:

$$
\begin{array}{r}
26 \\
- 25 \quad\quad \textbf{5} \quad \text{x 5} \\
\hline
1 \\
- 1 \quad\quad \textbf{0.2} \text{ x 5} \\
\hline
0 \quad\quad \textbf{5.2 x 5}
\end{array}
$$

5 + 0.2 = 5.2

The final answer is: **26 ÷ 5 = 5.2**

Another example: **55.5 ÷ 5**

$$\begin{array}{r} 55.5 \\ - \underline{50} \\ 5.5 \end{array}$$ **10** x 5

$$\begin{array}{r} - \underline{5} \\ 0.5 \end{array}$$ **1** x 5

$$\begin{array}{r} - \underline{0.5} \\ 0 \end{array}$$ **0.1** x 5
                                 11.1 x 5

10 + 1 + 0.1 = 11.1

The final answer is: **55.5 ÷ 5 = 11.1**

WORKSHEET D9

Complete these key value tables.

23 x1 =	106 x1 =	54 x1 =
23 x0.1 = 2.3	106 x0.1 =	54 x0.1 =
23 x0.2 =	106 x0.2 =	54 x0.2 =
23 x0.5 =	106 x0.5 =	54 x0.5 =

WORKSHEET D10

Key value multiples:
$$34 \times 0.5 = 17$$
$$34 \times 0.2 = 6.8 \quad \text{decimal multiples}$$
$$34 \times 0.1 = 3.4$$
$$34 \times 1 = 34$$
$$34 \times 2 = 68$$
$$34 \times 5 = 170 \quad \text{whole number multiples}$$
$$34 \times 10 = 340$$
$$34 \times 20 = 680$$

Use the key value multiples table above to answer these questions:

1) $683.4 \div 34$

2) $425 \div 34$

3) $1887 \div 34$

4) $581.4 \div 34$

5) $1720.4 \div 34$

6) $210.8 \div 34$

Division by multiplying

Division and multiplication are opposites, in the same way that addition and subtraction are opposites.

So, it is possible to subtract by adding on, for example:

$$83 - 27$$

Start with 27 and add on 3 $27 + 3 = 30$
Add on 50 $30 + 50 = 80$
Add on 3 $80 + 3 = 83$

Add up all the 'added on numbers': $3 + 50 + 3 = 56$

Answer: $83 - 27 = 56$

In our subtraction method for division we constructed a table of key multiple values and subtracted them from the number we have to divide to obtain an answer.

In a multiplication version we can add up key multiple values until we reach the value of the number we have to divide.

For example: $175 \div 7$

The table:

$$
\begin{array}{rcr}
1 \times 7 & = & 7 \\
2 \times 7 & = & 14 \\
5 \times 7 & = & 35 \\
10 \times 7 & = & 70 \\
20 \times 7 & = & 140 \\
\end{array}
$$

The answer is calculated by adding key multiples until we reach 175.

$$
\begin{array}{rl}
140 & \mathbf{20} \; \times 7 \\
+ \; 35 & + \; \mathbf{5} \; \times 7 \\
\hline
175 & \mathbf{25} \; \times 7
\end{array}
$$

$$25 \times 7 = 175$$

Answer: **175 ÷ 7 = 25**

A second example: **391 ÷ 17**

The table of key multiples:

$$
\begin{array}{rcl}
1 & \times \; 17 = & 17 \\
2 & \times \; 17 = & 34 \\
5 & \times \; 17 = & 85 \\
10 & \times \; 17 = & 170 \\
20 & \times \; 17 = & 340
\end{array}
$$

Now add the key multiples until the total is 391.

$$
\begin{array}{rl}
340 & \mathbf{20} \; \times 17 \\
+ \; 34 & \mathbf{2} \; \times 17 \\
\hline
374 & \\
+ \; 17 & + \; \mathbf{1} \; \times 17 \\
\hline
391 & \mathbf{23} \; \times 17
\end{array}
$$

$$23 \times 17 = 391$$

Answer: **391 ÷ 17 = 23**

WORKSHEET D11

Work out the answers to these division problems by **adding** key multiples.

$$
\begin{aligned}
1 \ \times\ 17 &= \ \ 17 \\
2 \ \times\ 17 &= \ \ 34 \\
5 \ \times\ 17 &= \ \ 85 \\
10 \ \times\ 17 &= \ 170 \\
20 \ \times\ 17 &= \ 340 \\
50 \ \times\ 17 &= \ 850
\end{aligned}
$$

1)   442 ÷ 17   2)   885 ÷ 17

3)   884 ÷ 17   4)   1275 ÷ 17

5)   289 ÷ 17   6)   1054 ÷ 17

A further explanation of the link between division and multiplication

When we calculate the area of a rectangle we multiply the lengths of the two sides.

For example:

12

5   Area = ?

The area is calculated by multiplying together the lengths of the two sides.

$$Area = 12 \times 5 = 60$$

If we knew the area and the length of one of the sides, we can calculate the length of the other side by division.

Length = ?

5   Area = 60

$$Length = 60 \div 5 = 12$$

The rectangle can be related to one of the ways we write out division.

$$\begin{array}{r} 12 \\ 5\overline{)60} \end{array} \quad \text{derives from} \quad \begin{array}{r} 12 \\ 5\overline{|60|} \end{array}$$

The rectangle image also explains why the order in which the numbers (the lengths of the sides) are multiplied does not affect the answer (the area).

It also explains that the number (length of a side) you select for the division (of the area) will affect the answer.

ACTIVITY D10

Set up the area, either with square counters or base ten blocks or squared paper, to show that the area is:

'12 lots of 5'   or   '12 columns of 5'

$$5+5+5+5+5+5+5+5+5+5 +5 +5 = 60$$

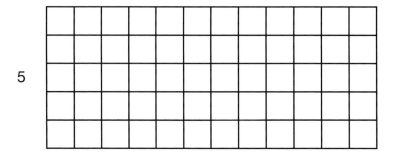

5

12

Then 'reverse' the demonstration to take away, or shade one column (of 5) at a time to show that the repeated subtraction of 5 gives the answer 12.

Division: the summary so far

- Division is about dividing a quantity up into a number of equal parts
- This can be done by repeated subtraction
- The repeated subtraction can be done with key value multiples
- It can also be done as the opposite operation, multiplication, using repeated addition
- Multiplication can be used to check the answer to a division question
- Multiplication can be used to estimate the answer to a division question

Division by numbers less than 1

The usual interpretation of an answer to a division is that the answer will be smaller than the starting number. This is not always true.

If a number is divided by a number less than 1, then the answer will be bigger than the starting number.

If we use the phrase, 'how many in?' we can start the process of understanding this outcome.

A half is less than 1. If we ask 'how many half pizzas in a whole pizza?' the answer is 2. Using the more abstract symbols we write:

$$1 \div \frac{1}{2} = 2$$

Since a half is less than 1, then we should expect to get more than one half pizza out of our whole (1) pizza. So, in this sense, we are dividing something that is bigger by something that is smaller and getting an answer that is more than 1.

So, it follows that the answer to 'how many half pizzas in three whole pizzas?' is 6.

$$3 \div \frac{1}{2} = 6$$

The smaller we make the dividing number, the bigger we make our answer. If we make the pizza slices smaller, say one quarter, then the question becomes, 'how many quarter pizzas in a whole pizza?' and the answer is 4.

In symbols this is:

$$1 \div \frac{1}{4} = 4$$

If the fractions are converted to decimals:

$$\frac{1}{2} = 0.5 \qquad \frac{1}{4} = 0.25$$

we will, obviously, get the same answers to the same questions:

$$1 \div 0.5 = 2$$

$$1 \div 0.25 = 4$$

This is another example of an ' opposite' when using operations.

When we multiply by numbers greater than 1 we get a bigger answer.

When we multiply by numbers less than 1 we get a smaller answer.

When we divide by numbers greater than 1 we get a smaller answer.

When we divide by numbers smaller than 1 we get a bigger answer.

For more on dividing by numbers less than 1 see 'What to do when you can't do fractions, decimals and percentages'.

A comparison of the traditional method for division and the key value multiples method

The division is: **5624 ÷ 37**

$$
\begin{array}{r}
152 \\
37\,)\overline{\,5624} \\
37 \\
\hline
192 \\
185 \\
\hline
74 \\
74 \\
\hline
0
\end{array}
$$

5624		
− 3700	**100**	
1924		
− 1850	**50**	
74		
− 74	**+ 2**	
0	**152**	

1	x 37 =	37
2	x 37 =	74
5	x 37 =	185
10	x 37 =	370
20	x 37 =	740
50	x 37 =	1850
100	x 37 =	3700

Answer: **5624 ÷ 37 = 152**

In this comparison, the number of steps is the same for both methods and the process is the same. It is the layout that is different.

A second example: **2701 ÷ 37**

$$
\begin{array}{r}
73 \\
37\,)\overline{\,2701} \\
259 \\
\hline
111 \\
111 \\
\hline
0
\end{array}
$$

2701	
−1850	**50**
851	
−740	**20**
111	
−74	**2**
37	
−37	**+1**
0	**73**

Anwser: **2701 ÷ 37 = 73**

In this example, the key value multiples method takes two extra steps, but the traditional method requires some difficult multiples, difficult to chose and difficult to calculate. For example you have to recognise that the nearest multiple to 270 is 7 x 37 = 259.

Both methods have their advantages. The main advantage of the key value multiples method is that you do not have to work out any complex multiples. If this skill is a weakness for you, then the key value multiples method will be more likely to lead to success. The key value multiples method provides a 'built in' estimate.

There are some reasons why the 'traditional' method may be difficult for some learners:

- You have to know all the basic times/multiplication facts, as division facts

- You have to be able to decide how many times a two or maybe three digit number divides into a number

- The layout is abstract. It does not self-explain

- The layout requires good spatial skills when writing

- There is no built-in estimate